SCARED

ANTHONY HOROWITZ

ADAPTED BY TONY LEE • ILLUSTRATED BY DAN BOULTWOOD

First published in 2010
by Franklin Watts

Cover design by Peter Scoulding

Franklin Watts
338 Euston Road
London NW1 3BH

Franklin Watts Australia
Level 17/207 Kent Street
Sydney, NSW 2000

A CIP catalogue record for this book
is available from the British Library.

ISBN: 978 0 7496 9511 8

1 3 5 7 9 10 8 6 4 2

Printed in China

Franklin Watts is a division of Hachette Children's Books,
an Hachette UK company.
www.hachette.co.uk

Gary Wilson was lost.
Stupid countryside! Stupid Suffolk! Stupid field!
He was also hot, tired and angry.
Where's the cottage! Hell, where is anything!
Why is Suffolk so flat?
All I see are fields, hedges and trees!
Cheers, Mum - for dragging me out of the city for this!

They should concrete over the whole thing!
You hear me? They should concrete over you! Turn you into a car park!
Hah. Suffolk as a giant car park. I'd pay to see that --
SPLAT!
@*$%#! These trainers cost a hundred quid!
It's gonna take ages to wash that off!
Mum can do it.
It's her fault I'm here anyway.

She's the one who dragged me here and dumped me in the middle of this.
I was perfectly comfortable in London! Gah!
I'll make her suffer, when I get back.
If I ever get back, that is!
HAHAH! LOOK AT GARY! HE'S LOST!
Who's there? Who said that?
STUPID GARY WILSON! HE HASN'T A CLUE WHERE HE IS!
Shut up! Nobody laughs at me!
Stop it! I'll get you back! I always get them back!
HAHAHA! LOST IN A FIELD! HE SHOULD HAVE LISTENED TO HIS GRAN!
Nobody laughs at Gary Wilson!

Then.
You hear me? Nobody!
I'm sorry, Gary! I wasn't laughing at you!
Sorry what, Peters?
You're sorry... what?
SLAP!
Ow! Okay! I'm - I'm...
...I'm sorry, King Gary.
Haha! Look at the little girl!
Are you crying, Peters? Are they tears? Go play with your dolly!
What's this? Looks like a new book.
Is that right, Peters? Did Mummy buy you some nice, new textbooks this term?

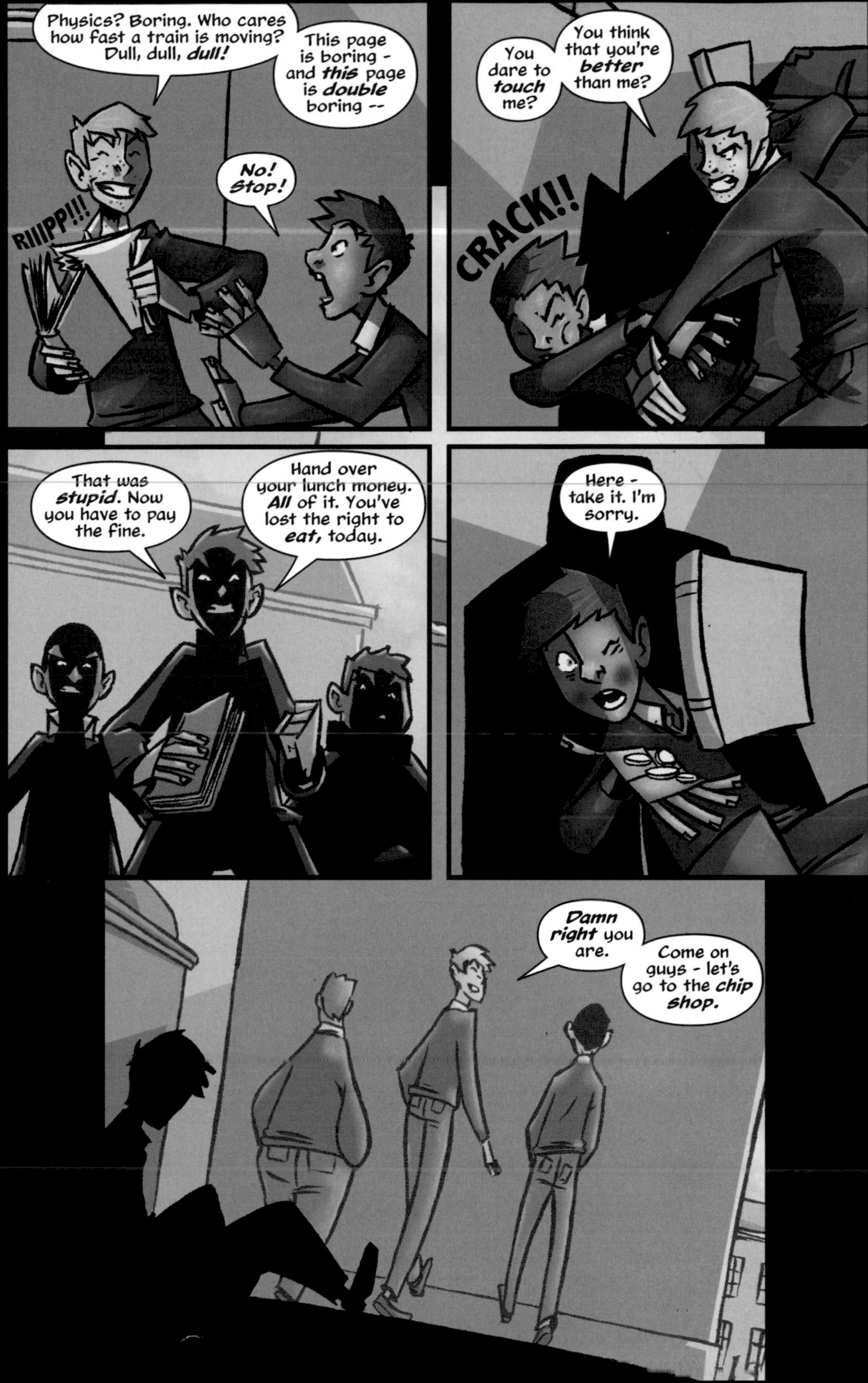
Physics? Boring. Who cares how fast a train is moving? Dull, dull, dull!
This page is boring - and this page is double boring --
RIIIPP!!!
No! Stop!
You dare to touch me?
You think that you're better than me?
CRACK!!
That was stupid. Now you have to pay the fine.
Hand over your lunch money. All of it. You've lost the right to eat, today.
Here - take it. I'm sorry.
Damn right you are.
Come on guys - let's go to the chip shop.

Now.
I hate nature! You hear me? I hate you!
Pah! I wish I had a machete! Or an axe!
I'd sort you out once and for --
Arrghh!!
$*&%+ branch! Damn thorns!
You cut me! You cut me!
Think you're clever, do you?
Nobody makes me look like a fool! Even if you're only a branch!
SNAP!!!

Yeah! Don't mess with Gary Wilson!
Is that all you've got? Come on! I can take it!
CLUMP!
Whoa --
THUMP!!
Hah! You think this is supposed to scare me?
You know nothing about how to scare someone! I'm an expert!

Then.
Wilson! Get here! Now!
squad

Yes sir? What did I do this time?
I'm getting reports of bullying, Wilson!
Extortion, damage to school property - you name it, I'm hearing it!

Is that all, sir? Because I've got a football game that I'm playing in --
No that isn't all! If I hear one more complaint about you, I'm going to --

-- You'll do what?

Well, you'll be getting detention - that's for starters --
Detention? And that's supposed to scare me?
I eat detentions for breakfast, you four-eyed moron!

Now look here, Wilson --
No, you look here. I'm King Gary and I rule this school.
You work here by my permission, not the other way round.
I could punch you, beat you - and there's nothing you can do about it.
Because all I have to do is go 'please sir, teacher hit me' and you're out of here.
Fired. Unemployed. Alone.
There are rules, you see. Rules that stop you touching, hurting a student.
I love to break rules. And I'm a good liar. Who do you think the school board would believe?
So - the next time you threaten King Gary with anything -
- I'll be crying wolf faster than you can scream 'industrial tribunal'. You got me?
Yes, yes I do, Wilson.
Good. And there goes the bell.
No dilly dallying now! Don't you have a class to go to?

Now.
Pye Hall has to be around here!
I didn't walk that far off the path!
Make sure you follow the footpaths, Gary.
And don't forget the Country Code. You don't want to get lost now, do you?
Country code. Hah. Yeah, like that's anything more than a guideline for sad old ramblers.
Stupid, mad old bat --
-- Whoa!!
SNAP!

Ow.
Ow.
Ow.
WHAM!

My leg! Argh! It's broken!

Well, maybe not broken -
- but I've definitely twisted my ankle!

And great - a storm's coming.

Then.
It was a heart attack, they said. Happened suddenly at work.
The other tellers at the bank saw him just fall over, dead!
He was ⫸sob⫷ he was still holding the date stamp in his hand when they found him!
That's terrible Jane! I'm so sorry!
And this must be a terrible blow to young Gary! To be the man of the house at such an early age!
Huh? Yeah, whatever. I never got on with Dad anyway.
I don't really miss him.
The bank were good to us - but the pension isn't enough to keep us going -
- so I'm going to have to go back to work.

And after all - Gary does like his creature comforts!
What would you do without --
What have I told you about touching the hair?
I don't like it when you do that!
I'm - I'm sorry, darling. I forgot.
That's your problem, isn't it? You always forget.
Forget my breakfast, forget to clean my room --
He's - he's just grieving. He doesn't mean it.
No, really. He's a good boy sometimes.

Now.
Hnf - nnng - ow!

And of course I didn't bring an umbrella.
It wasn't cloudy when I left!

Hnng - it's definitely twisted. Great.
Well, it'd better sort itself out before the playoffs next week!

How long does it rain out here, anyway?

HSSSSSSTT!
Still, could be worse --
GAH!!!
Argh! Get them off me! Ow!
Not spiders! Anything but spiders!
Good - the rain's stopped.
Which way is it now?

Then.
Pye Hall. Suffolk.
You promised me that we'd go to Ibiza this year!
No, dear - you told me we would be going to Ibiza.
And I told you that the best that we could afford was a trip to see my mother - your gran - twice a year!
I wish I only had to see you twice a year.
NO SMOKING
You hate me. You do this because you don't like me.
You never give me what I ask for.
What about those trainers? I bought you those!
They cost me over a hundred pounds!

Yeah? Well I wanted the blue and gold ones!
These ones were last season's!
I'm sorry, darling - but those ones were double the price.
I simply couldn't afford them. Maybe next time.
Next time. It's always next time.
Next time we'll go to Ibiza. But this time we'll go see my mad old gran on a farm in the middle of nowhere.
NO SMOKING
Gary! You're not allowed to smoke on the train!
Like I really care what you, or anyone else thinks.

Now.
All I want is a *signpost!* Is that too much to ask for?

What the --
RIIIPP!!!

My jacket! I can't believe this!
This cost a fortune!

Well - it would have if I hadn't *stolen* it from the shop!

Stupid tree - you should watch where you're going --
-- Those tree trunks look like *faces!*
Now that's just *creepy.*
I'm not *scared* - I'm too *angry* to be scared.
But there's definitely something *weird* that's happening here -
- and I bet that it's connected to *Gran.*

Then.
Look at it! *Pye Hall!*
Isn't it *beautiful,* Gary!
A two-hour train ride and a cab into the middle of *nowhere...*
...Doesn't make a broken down cottage *beautiful,* Mum.

I was so *happy* here, once!
Here you go - keep the change.

I'll have the change, thanks.
She didn't *mean* that.

There she is!
Welcome home, Jane!
Hello, Mum! It's so good to be back!
You're looking thinner, Jane. And you're tired.
You've got no colour at all!
Mum, I'm fine!
No you're not, you don't look well. But a week in the country will soon sort you out!
And look at you, Gary - you've grown so much!
Hi, Gran. I'm starving.
What have you got to eat around here?

Now.
Come on! I know I had it in my pocket earlier!
Where is that #%&* chocolate!
So hungry! There must be something I can eat!
If the SAS can live out here for weeks, I can manage a couple of hours!
Aha! Now that's what I'm talking about!
A nice feast of berries!
Fit for a King!

Mmm! That's good!
Wha --
Poisonous -
Whuurrpp!!
Feel... sick...
Hate the... country...

Then.
A week in the country will do you the world of good!
Fresh air, some peace and quiet --
What's so good about the country, anyway?
No, seriously. Where's the fast-food takeaway? How about the five-a-side pitch?
Do you guys even understand what the Internet is here?
You guys wouldn't recognise a nightclub if you saw one.
Gary! Apologise to your gran right now!
It's okay, Jane - he's young. He doesn't understand yet.
Everything is different in the country, Gary.

Is this another speech on flowers and the trees and nature?
The country is full of people with no life at all!
You float along with time, here. You don't feel time rushing past you.
You can stand out here and imagine how things were before people spoiled everything with their noise; their machines.
You can still feel the magic of the countryside.
Hah! Why would I want to remember before machines existed?
What possible reason would there be to imagine a world before MP3s, HDTV, mobile phones and on-line gaming!
Don't mock the magic, Gary.
It might just mock you back.

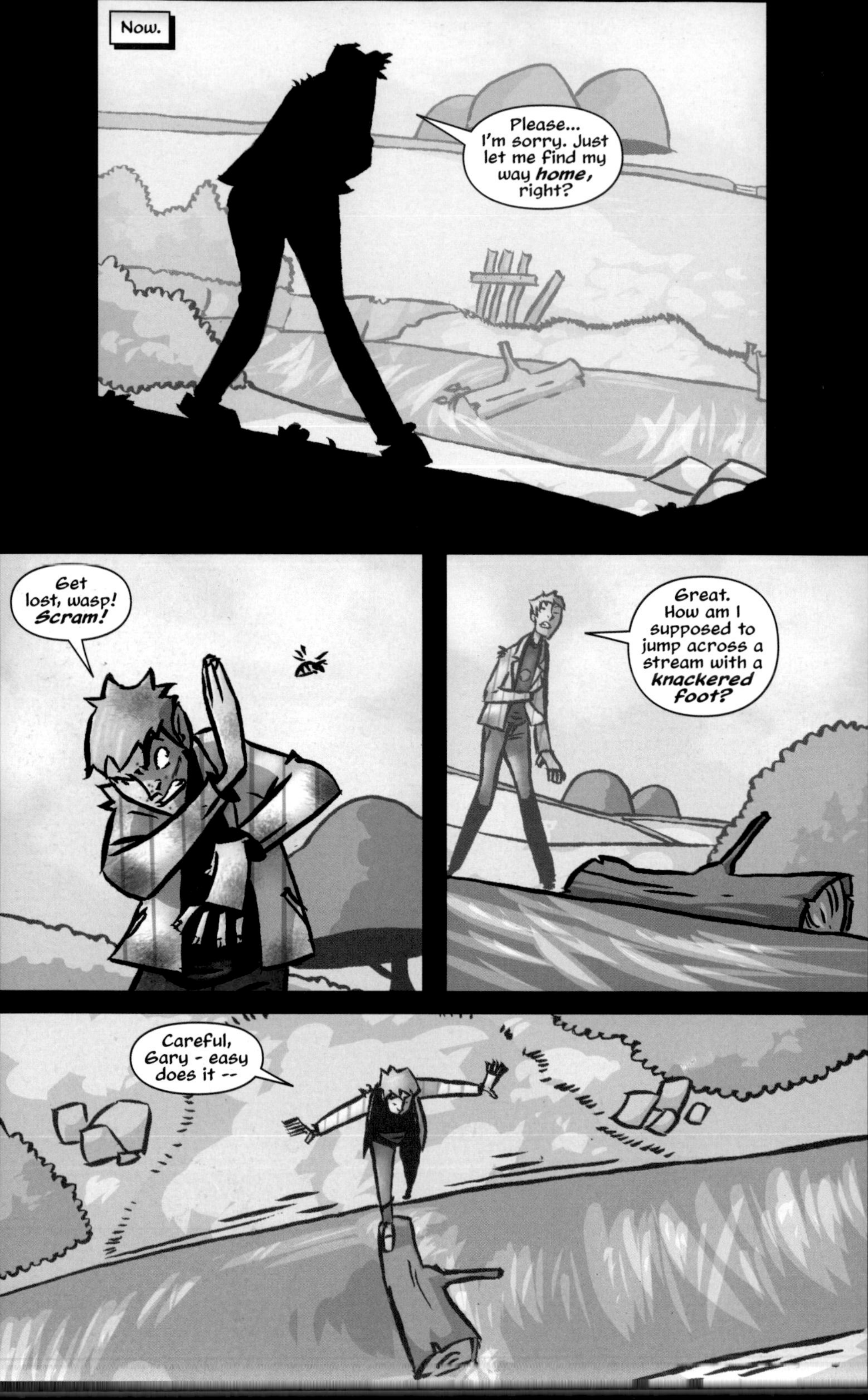
Now.
Please... I'm sorry. Just let me find my way *home,* right?
Get lost, wasp! *Scram!*
Great. How am I supposed to jump across a stream with a *knackered foot?*
Careful, Gary - easy does it --

Hey!
I said get lost, wasp!
I mean --
Whoa --
SPLASH!!!
That's just great. Wonderful.
I hate you, countryside. Hate you.

Then.
The power of Mother Nature is all around you, Gary.
It's alive - and it's waiting --
Waiting for what? You're going senile, old lady!
All this talk of 'magic' and 'Mother Nature'!
There's no magic in the countryside! Only days that seem to drag on forever -
- and nights with nothing to do!
'Mother Nature' - that's a good one! Even if the old girl had existed -
- which is very unlikely, let's face it --
Gary - stop --
I said don't touch me!

CRASH!!
Gary! That was your own mother!
What were you thinking!
Yeah, well - she shouldn't have touched me!
All your stupid talk of magic - it annoyed me!
Mother Nature was finished off long ago by the cities!
Buried under miles of concrete motorways! Hah!
Driving along one at 100mph with the music blaring and the roof open --
-- Now that would be real magic!
You stupid, arrogant, ignorant little child --
-- You come down here, turn on your own mother and then lecture me about magic?
You have no idea what you've unleashed, boy.
Dark Magics.

Now.
Dark magic. Hah!
You hear that, 'Mother Nature'? I laugh at your magic! I spit on your 'Country Code'!
Now show me the way home!
Hey! You there! I - I see you!
Hey! Come back here!
Don't make me come after you! I just need to know directions home!
THWIPP!!

CRASH!!
ARGHHH!!!
Come back!
Argh! $%#!@ Wasp! That hurt!
I'll kill you, too!
Help me! All I want to do is get home!
My mum - she'll be worried by now!

Earlier.
What goes around comes around, Gary!
Do you think you can live your life like this and not have to pay any dues?
Hamburgers! Concrete roads! Shopping malls and beer!
That's what the country needs!
Mother, please - he's just a boy!
He's nothing but a bully! And he's no grandson of mine!
The countryside sees you for what you truly are, Gary. Remember that!
You're both so boring!
I'm going for a walk!
And do what? Smoke some of those cigarettes you bought -
- with the money I saw you steal from your mother's purse yesterday?
You're a mad old witch. And your magic stories are for children!

Just make sure you follow the *footpaths*, Gary.
And don't forget the *Country Code*. You don't want to get *lost* now, do you?
SLAM!
sob I'm so sorry, Mother - he's a good boy, really!
But even though he's all I've got - sometimes I wish that I was *alone!*
He's a *thug*. And you'd be best off *without* him if he's going to act like *that* to family.
But don't worry - one day he'll *step off the path* --
-- And what goes around *will* come around.

Now.
Why won't you *help* me?
Stop playing games! I'm *hurt!* I broke my leg! I got *stung!*

I'm cut and I'm wet - and *all I want is my mum!*
And my cigarettes are soaked!

I'm gonna *catch* you!
I *see* you! I see where you're going!

You think that a stile is - *hnf* - gonna *stop* me?
Even with a bad leg I'll --

Argh!!! Stinging nettles!
Arghh!!! That *hurts!* They hurt so much!
Why are you doing this to me!
Please... All I want to do is --
-- Get home.

Then.
'Remember the Country Code, Gary'.
Like I care about the Country Code, Gran.
I mustn't litter, must I? That's against the Code.
Whoops!
PUNT!
SNAP!
Of course, I wouldn't dare break anything. That would be wrong.
Where's your dark magic now, you mad bat? Eh?
Whoops - that was bad of me.
After all, I'd hate to see any of this lovely countryside go up in flames.

I'm sure that I forgot something. Was it to shut this gate?
Surely the Country Code would tell me to do that?
Oh, I do hope that no farm animals escape through that open gate -
- and get mown down by a tractor!
Screech! Bam! Instant steak!
And of course, Gran, we've got your favourite code of all.
Make sure you follow the footpaths, Gary.
And don't forget the Country Code. You don't want to get lost now, do you?
To hell with you, Gran.
I ain't scared of anything.

Now.
Found them. This is all their fault. They should have stopped me leaving.
Perhaps they'll think twice about how lovely the countryside is --
-- When they see their precious little cottage go up in smoke.
It's so hot... I need to stop for a bit...
Hold on! It's him! The joker who's been playing me for a fool!
We'll see who the fool is now!
- hnf - Oi! You! Yeah, that's right! I'm talking to you!
What kind of game do you think you're playing, eh? You think that I'm scared of you?
You've got the wrong boy if you're trying to be scary -
- Huh?

POTATOE
I don't understand! I saw you! I followed you!
I even followed you here! I --
You have no idea what you've unleashed, boy.
Dark Magics.
-- I walked off the path again.
Ow! What's that sticking in my hair...
...Straw?

Arrghh!! Where did the straw come from!
My ankle - it's killing me --

Arrgghh!! My leg! It's wood!

Help memmph!

Mm! Mmmph!!! Mm!!

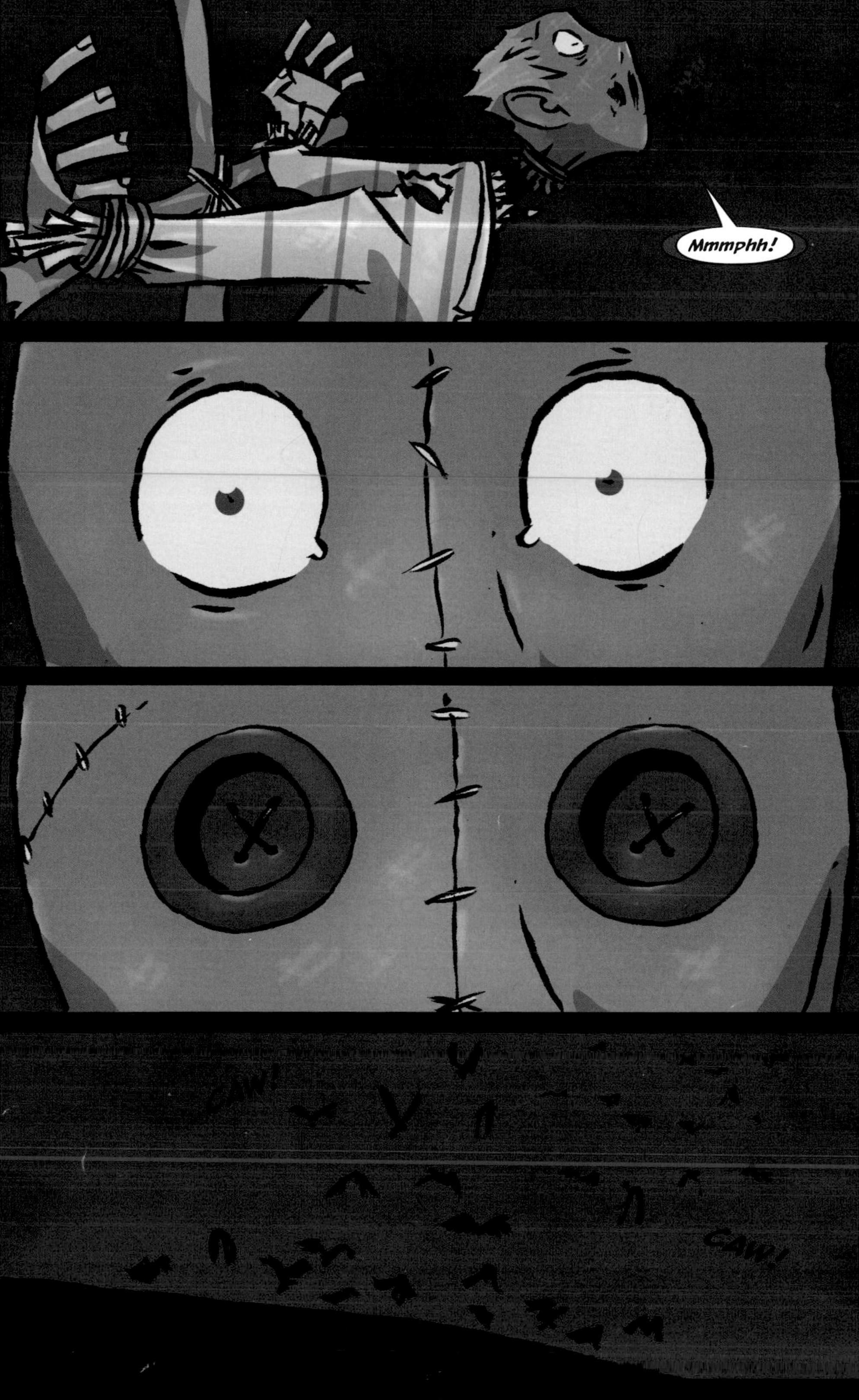
Mmmphh!
CAW!
CAW!

The police looked for Gary for five days - but there was no trace of him.
I'm sorry, Mrs Wilson - he could have been abducted, run away - anything.
Strange, to disappear completely like that --
-- It's like the countryside took him and swallowed him up.
A week later he watched his mother leave Pye Hall and return to London.
Let me know if you hear anything, Mum.
He was glad she had the decency to cry, mourning her loss.
But he couldn't help feeling that she looked rather less tired and ill than she had before.
Mmmmph...

...Gary?
No. Just a scarecrow. Doing what he does best.
Being scary.
Just like Gary used to be.

"You have no idea what you've unleashed, boy. Dark magics."
"You know nothing about how to scare someone! I'm an expert!"
End.